The Odd Squa

KEEP CALM
and
LAUGH
at
CHRISTMAS

by Allan Plenderleith

RAVETTE PUBLISHING

First published in 2017 by
Ravette Publishing Limited
PO Box 876, Horsham, West Sussex RH12 9GH
info@ravettepub.co.uk

ISBN: 978-1-84161-403-8

Printed and bound in India by Replika Press Pvt. Ltd.

Santa makes his delivery to the Chav district.

Oh dear. It appeared the chocolate advent calendar Mum bought Billy was from a faulty batch.

Everyone on the naughty list gets a little something extra from Santa on Christmas Eve.

Moira had asked for a Barbie for Christmas.

Having slipped on the ice, Lily realised she'd broken a joint.

Alf wasn't really getting into the
spirit of their game of charades.

Jeff discovers some dangerous
cookies on his computer.

This wasn't what Billy meant
when he said he
wanted a dog for Christmas.

After weeks of being
pestered, Santa finally gives his
employees a raise.

Jeff wasn't exactly impressed by today's modern carol singers.

At Christmas, Jeff likes to leave the newspaper boy a tip.

Maude finally discovered a place the kids would NEVER go to look for their Christmas presents.

Suddenly, Rudolf realised he was going bald.

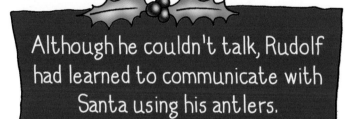

Although he couldn't talk, Rudolf had learned to communicate with Santa using his antlers.

On Christmas morning, Billy could spot all the little tell-tale signs that Santa had been.

Because of the warmer winters,
Santa has had to adapt his outfit.

Unfortunately, Jeff had bought
a Santa-nav.

As Maude got undressed, she shook off
the feeling she was being watched – safe
in the knowledge she was 20 storeys high.

Jeff makes sure he doesn't get another pair of socks for Christmas.

Somehow, whilst they were in the kitchen, the turkey had disappeared.

With the help of a couple of spare elves, Mrs Claus gets a perky new look.

Jeff wasn't sure – but the Christmas tree appeared to be smiling.

OK, so the sudden change in temperature meant Frosty had no face – but at least now he was a MAN!

Rather than admit she'd had
a little accident, Lily opens up
an impromptu ice rink.

Nigel – the brown-nosed reindeer.

As far as Maude was concerned there was
no such thing as too many Christmas lights.

Dug's mates always wanted to
get mashed up at Christmas.

What happens when you don't leave
the newspaper boy a Christmas tip.

When the Christmas tree fairy
goes to the loo.

Maude was about to
unwrap yet another
disappointing
Christmas present.

When Santa went to
the red light district.

Ladies – to confuse men on cold weather days, simply pour a packet of Maltesers down your blouse.

Whilst working on his PC,
Santa had a
problem with his server.

For Christmas, Jeff treats himself
to a honey-coated ham.

Maude likes a
ginger bread man
at Christmas.

This year's best-selling
gift for guys.

For Christmas,
Jeff receives something
he'll never part with.

Rude Olf.

What happens when
you stop believing in
Father Christmas.

As Maude was a keen wine buff,
Jeff treated her to a full-bodied 69
after Christmas dinner.

How they loved Christmas Day –
Jeff would admire Maude's stockings
while she fiddled around with his baubles.

Jeff really stuffed himself
on Christmas Day.

"That's what I think of Christmas,"
said Jeff.

"Weigh Two Deer!"

Apple have brought out a
new device for Geordies.

Santa gets a brazilian.

"Bloody things are everywhere,"
grumbled Santa.

Billy knew exactly what to give
the lady collecting for the
old folks home.

Soon, Billy would become a
life member of the naughty list.

Santa curses the invention of email.

Jeff's Christmas wish came true –
just not how he expected.

Jeff discovers the benefits of genetically modified turkey.

Lily gets rid of the carol singers
once and for all.

Lily comes up with a clever way
to carry all her Christmas shopping.

Suddenly the wise men regretted
buying the cheap sat nav.

This year, Jeff was finally prepared for the carol singers.

Jeff told Maude he'd hidden a surprise Christmas present for her in the tree.

Snowed in for days over Christmas, at least Maude had enough provisions to keep her sustained.

Things just weren't the same
since Santa got sponsorship.

Santa suddenly realises the
ad for new elves has been misspelt.

Rudolf had become much better
behaved since Santa tied the reins
somewhere else.

It was true – 4x4s are bad
for our environment.

When making the gravy for the
Christmas dinner, always remember to
add plenty of wine.

The cat hoped Maude would buy
an artificial Christmas tree next year.

Jeff's thoughts always turned to
those he missed on Christmas Day.

Jeff gets one up on
the neighbour.

The credit crunch has even
hit Santa.

Rudolf could never understand why
it was always Cupid that got the girls.

When Billy pulled the cracker with
Granny, the bang didn't come
from where he expected.

Once again on Christmas Eve,
Santa is stopped by the police.